GW00870200

IRONFIST CHINMI

Attack of the Black Flame

Takeshi Maekawa

Bloomsbury

CONTENTS

5

1
Dear Chinmi,
I hope you are well.

It's been nearly a year since you went off to the Dailin Temple.

2
I'm fine, of course, same as always.

3
It would have been hard for me here without you but Uncle and Aunty have been very helpful.

4
I don't imagine you can get time off from training to come and see me, so, instead, your big sister is coming to see you at the Dailin Temple!
No real reason, just to say hello...

5
So I'll be along seven days after I send this letter. See you then...
Your sister,
Mei Ling.

⑥ My sister's coming to visit in seven days!!

⑦ Oh! Really?

⑧ That's... great.

⑨ Seven days after the letter...

⑩ That will be the day after tomorrow!

⑪ By now she must have got as far as Song Jia village over the mountain.

⑫ Heeheehee. My sister's really coming here!

⑬ I'm a bit worried about a young girl travelling on her own like that. Why don't you go and meet her? I think that might be a good idea.

④ I'm sure the Abbot won't mind.

③ Young Chinmi, your sister readily gave her consent for you to come to the Dailin Temple.

② Is it really OK for me to go and meet her?

① Eh!

⑦ Chinmi, be careful.

⑥ Well, I'll be off...

⑩ Jin Tan'll spit teeth if he finds out I've been **allowed** to skip classes.

⑨ You know what? I think he could easily manage a four-league race!

⑧ SEE YOU!

12 I can't believe a whole year has passed.

11 Amazing.

16 Gokuwai...

15 Eek.

14 Eek eek.

13 I didn't write for all that time! Mei Ling must have been worried...

20 Oh. You want to see Mei Ling too.

19 Eek eek.

17 EEK!

boing

18 What're you doing here?

13

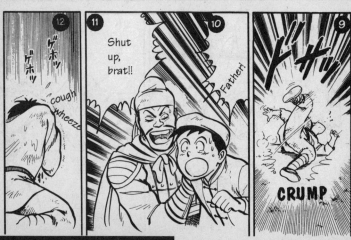

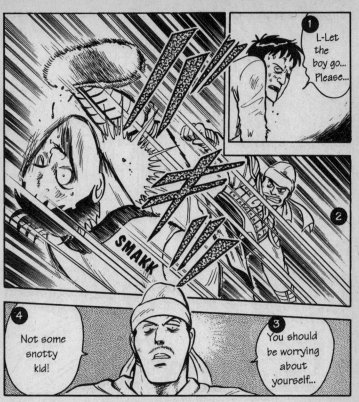

9

8

Hhhr-hh

wheeze

10

Father!!

plik

14
...this will
be a whole
lot more
effective.

13
If they
can see
him
too...

12
He must be
able to see
the whole
village from
there!

Hehehehe
Hahaha

11
What a
lovely
view, eh?

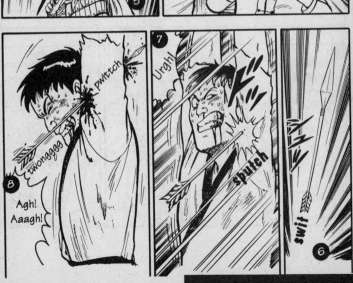

18

19

20

SPLAT

Huh?!

donk

21

① Who the hell are you lot?!

② Do you have any idea of what you're doing?!

④ Temple boy...

⑤ Do **you** have any Idea who we are?

⑥ No! Should I?

③

What is going on here?

What is this kid doing here?

Lord Ryuhi!!

klop...
klop.

23

klomp

I can offer no explanation, my lord...

A monk!

Let me show you.

Do you know what happens to the enemies of the Black Flame?

plink

Wh...what is it?

24

26

CARRUMP
CARRUMP

!!

FOOSH

SWISH

28

Hhhr-hhr
Hhhr-
hhr

blungggg

Don't
forget
it!!

thwick

Do you see,
little monk? No
one stands
against the Black
Flame and lives
to tell
the tale...

36

In a few days...

...this village too will have ceased to exist.

HA HA HA HA

How do you want to do this one, Brother Zangi?

5 I'm running out of patience, Dohko.

6 barrum barrum

7 Zangi! Dohko! Sorry I'm late!

8 Ryuhi. At last!

Now I see, young Chinmi...

They're an evil gang of bandits, led by three brothers, Ryuhi, Zangi and Dohko. Every one of them is as bad as can be. There's not a good bone in any of their bodies!

What are we going to do, Mayor?

The Black Flame are on the move again.

What is this Black Flame?

② Get him in the heart! Go for a bull's-eye!
Ha ha ha ha.
You'll never do it!!

① They attack unsuspecting towns, kill the inhabitants and pillage their possessions! They are vile thieves and murderers.

④ We heard that all three brothers had been seen.

③ Several days ago, some of the Black Flame gang was sighted at a village to the east of here...

⑤ They didn't leave a single house standing in the last place they attacked!

① Mayor!

② What is it?

③ There's a letter from the Black Flame!!

④ A letter?

⑤ rustle

⑥ !!

⑦ tremble

⑧ shwackle

Song Jia village should be just over the next ridge.

7 No need to hurry. I can see Chinmi tomorrow.

6 I'll rest in Song Jia tonight.

5 Not much farther to go!

9 I bet he's better than ever at Kung Fu now.

8 He must have changed a lot over the past year.

10

klopp

Well,
look
at
that.

Ha,
Ha
Ha

48

④
Dailin Temple is not far from Song Jia.

50

⑤ The Black Flame have kidnapped a girl on the ridge!!

④ It's started!

⑦ No!... Whose daughter is she?

⑥ What!!?

⑪ Poor thing! Imagine, falling into the hands of the Black Flame!

⑩ She must have been a traveller.

⑧ Nobody from this village. Don't know...

⑨ Ah... well...

❹ Does that mean anything to anyone?

❸ I found her pack on the ridge. It has the name Mei Ling written on it.

❷ Don't tell me it's...

❶ Oh no...

❺ **NO!**

❻ They've got my sister!!

The End of Chapter One

52

Chapter Two
A Stab in the Dark

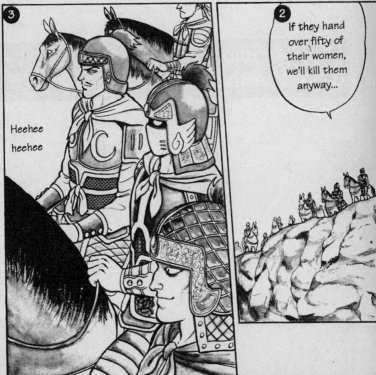

55

The same
fate awaits
all those
who go
over the
ridge.

A
HEAD!!

. . . .
. . . .

So what!?
Even if we
did they'd
probably
kill us
anyway!

The Black Flame
say they'll kill us
all unless we hand
over fifty of our
girls to them!

I say we
do what
we're told!

① Song Jia Mountain

② Chinmi? Where do you think you're going?

③ It's dangerous to go outside the walls, you know.

④ Yes, but this is important.

⑤ Well, come back quickly.

⑥ I don't think I can rely on the villagers for help. I'll have to save Mei Ling by myself.

⑦ But I can see why they're all so scared of the Black Flame...

⑨ I can see by the light of the moon.

⑩ scrape

⑧ There has to be a way.

rustle

3 Gokuwa! Sshh! Don't make a sound!

4 You surprised me...

Eek?

Eek!

5 We've got to move fast! We must help Mei Ling before dawn!

7 !!

Hahaha

Waaaha

hahaha

hahah

6

Hahahaa
Hahahaa

Waaaahahahaha

63

5

6

Looks like they're well tanked up!

7

pachik

10

DOH!

9

Who's there!?

8

11

Well!

chak chak

12

Are you going to come out?

13

I can't fight him, it'll bring the others!

chik

SMASH

KRIIIP

And if I stay in the open, I'm diced Chinmi for sure!

I can't hide behind anything! He'd just slice straight through it!

74

75

Is that the best you can do, temple boy?

Somehow I've got to get past that trident!!

hhhr-hhr
hhhr-hhr

Nowhere to run...

Ah!

④ Dammit...

⑦ Say your prayers...

⑥ Got it! If I can get him to stab deep into this screen...

His trident will be stuck!

YAAAAGH!

⑩ おおおおお

⑧ Do your worst, Scut Head!!

⑨ Come on!

⑨ Oh Chinmi! All this for me!

⑧ What's happened in there?

⑦ The light went out!

⑪ hhr-hhr

Why bother putting the candles out?!

⑩

⑭ THERE!

THWIP

⑬ You must be...

⑫ Just makes it more fun for me!

THAK

He can't see me! That was just lucky!

3

blup

2

!

1

chik

chonk

6
You don't have to make a sound for me to guess at your movements.

5
It's luck! It has to be luck!

4
Hahaha... You're just too easy to spot.

8
There's no way he'd be able to guess where I was in the dark!
No way!

7
He's bluffing!

chik

I didn't say a word! But Ryuhi found me anyway! There's no way for me to hide from him!!

If this goes on, I'm a dead man!!

Everything!

I have to HIDE completely! I have to hide all traces of me!! Movements, breathing...

1

2 ····!

3 Master Tiandao!

4 Listen Chinmi...

5 If you could truly slow your heart...

6 You would lose the aura of humanity...

7 Yes... I remember...

⑩ And he won't be able to track me...

⑨ I can turn to stone...

⑪ OK.

⑧ Chinmi! You must turn to stone!!

⑭ I am becoming as stone!

⑬ I am emptying my thoughts.

⑫ My heart is slowing.

2

plink

1

3

Nothing is in my mind...I am thinking of nothing, but nothing...I *am* nothing...

5

NO!
Slow my heart...

6

Don't think of the consequences...

4

But if he hears me...

7 Slow...

8 Slower...

9

11 I can't sense him anymore...

10 That's strange...

14 I can't believe it...

15 That little monk!!

12 He can't have sneaked out of the room.

13 So why have his signs stopped?

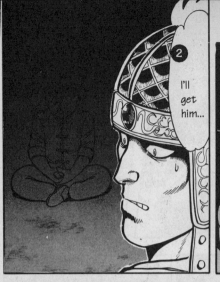

OR HOW
ABOUT
HERE!?

SWOOSH

6

Not there either.

5

No.

4

THOKK

8

plok plok

7

コ゛ハ゛ツ
KRAKK

10

phew

SWOOSH

9

DAMN!

11

What was that?

plat

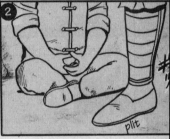

plit

plink

NOW!!

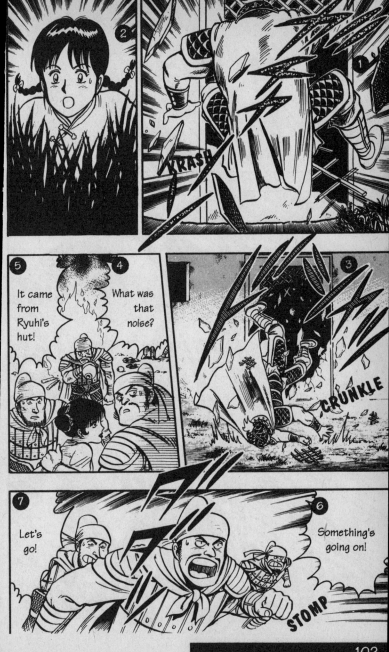

The End of Chapter Two

Chapter Three
Shockwave Kung Fu

107

What are they doing!?

It's all around the village!

① fsssh

② If they light that straw we'll be smoked out!!

③ They'll force us out of the village and cut us down outside the walls!!

④

⑤ Get on with it! My patience is short.

⑥ D'you hear!?

1

2 There's someone coming.

3 It's that brat again.

4

5

6

7 Are you the one who broke into Ryuhi's hut last night?

1 You may look like a little kid, but you don't act like one, temple boy.

2 You're a monk with a mission.

3 Zangi! What's going on here! Stop kidding around and start acting like a bandit!

SHLUP

4 This little squirt has just stood in front of the whole Black Flame, and challenged their leader to single combat!

5 Indulge me, Dohko, as I have indulged you.

6

7

clonk

clonk

8

11 As you wish.

10 If I win, I want you to promise not to attack Song Jia village!

9 There's something else I have to say!

12

14

13

16 The rest of the Black Flame should be a pushover!

15 If you can defeat me...

HYAAAAA AAAAGH

Wow! He's powerful!!

Watch your step!

I know!

I won't be as stupid as Ryuhi!

HYAGH!

120

THWACK

SWIP

Hee
hee...

Was **that** it!? You'll have to do a lot better than...

Hmm!

Urgh!!

CRUNK

126

9 I have shot the fire of *Qi* through your body...

8 Allow me to explain.

7 Shockwave Kung Fu?!

cough cough wheeze

10 Hhhr-hhr Hhhr~

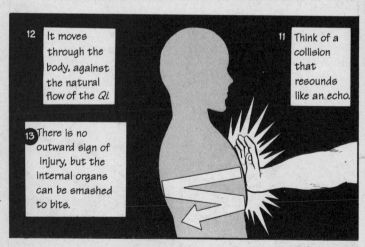

12 It moves through the body, against the natural flow of the *Qi.*

11 Think of a collision that resounds like an echo.

13 There is no outward sign of injury, but the internal organs can be smashed to bits.

2 ...without showing on the outside?

1 Is there a Kung Fu that can attack the inside...

3 Try it if you don't believe me! Haha!

SPLOT

4

Plonk

⑥

⑤ What kind of rubbish is this? Nothing happened! I could have chopped that melon in half!

CHOP

⑧

⑦ So far, you have felt only the most basic technique of Shockwave Kung Fu.

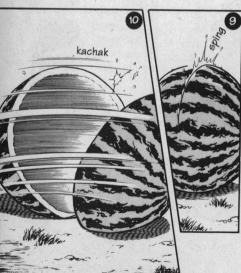

kachak

⑩

sping

⑨

splurch

5 ...shock waves resonate in both directions.

4 When I apply the force of my hands...

2 The inside of the melon has been completely pulped!

6 It's enough to turn the inside of the melon to mush!

7
cough
cough

8
I can't beat him...
I can hardly move!

Oof.

9
Lord Zangi!
What shall I
do with him?

10
I don't
think we
should kill
him yet.

11
I don't
think he'll
be able
to run
very far
tonight.

12
He'll still
be trying
to hold
his
insides
in!

13
I'm going to
make him
suffer ten
times as
much as
Ryuhi!

14
One night
will not
be enough!

138

Sleep well, temple boy!

I'm still
alive!

142

8 At dawn tomorrow, we shall execute him in front of his village!

10

11 OOF

9 How long can it be till dawn!?

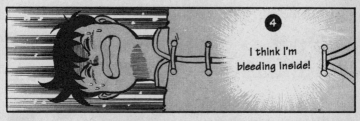

2

Hhhr hhr

3

splish splosh

Hhhr hhr

1

It hurts!

6

slurp...

5

4

Hhhr-hhr

9

Is there no way I can fight Shockwave Kung Fu?

8

Hhhr hhr hhhr hhr

7

12 What can I do?

Hhhr Hhhr Hhhr hhr

10 Zangi's attack is too unusual to counter in the normal way...

11 I don't think my body will recover from today's damage by dawn...

14 bleaak

13 URGH!

19

18 Plik Plik

17 plok plok plok

16

15 plok plok plok plok ポタ ポタ

The falling water is wearing away the stone..

plok
plok

148

1

2 What do you mean?

3 Do you know how it happens?

4 Something to do with the rain, right?

5 Yes...

6 The rain falls, and drop by drop it hits the same point on the stone...over and over again.

7 After many, many decades, the constant droplets eventually carve their own little dent.

8

9 It's just like Kung Fu. It takes many years of study to achieve one's aims.

10 Err... does it?

12 Over time, the weak rain drops build up into a powerful force.

11 The rain only carves the hole if it concentrates on one specific point.

14 For example, in Kung Fu you are taught to concentrate all of your power behind your punch. The whole body is punching, but the power is concentrated in the fist.

13 Concentration can equal strength.

15 When that tiny part of you hits your opponent, it strikes with the force of your entire mass. The power is concentrated in that tiny area.

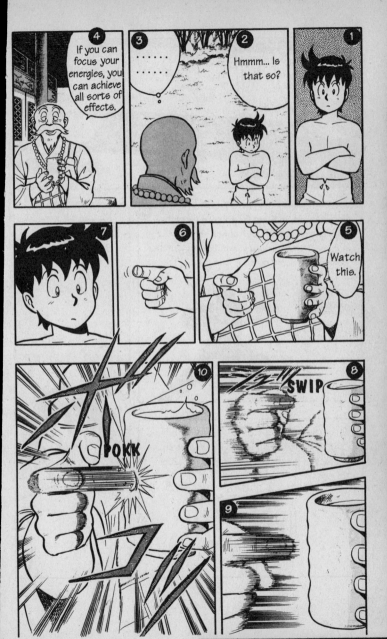

152

13. Huh! You just punched a hole in a tea cup with your finger!

12. glurg glurg glurg glurg

11.

15. If a child like you could do that, you would have the force of an adult...

14. Yes. I can do this because I have spent many years practising the focussing of energies for specific tasks.

18. I said you'd have to PRACTISE, Chinmi.

17. Hee hee.

16. How did he do that?

donk donk

153

2 Hmmm... Focussing of energy, eh?

4 I can't beat Zangi the way I am, but if I could find a fault, and then concentrate my efforts there.

5 But what could I do?

3 If you concentrate small power in a tiny area, its effect is like that of greater energy.

7 This will have to do!

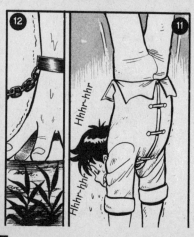

Phew! Next comes just four fingers.

Hhhr-hhr
Hhhr-hhr

Hhhr-hhr
Hhhr-hhr

155

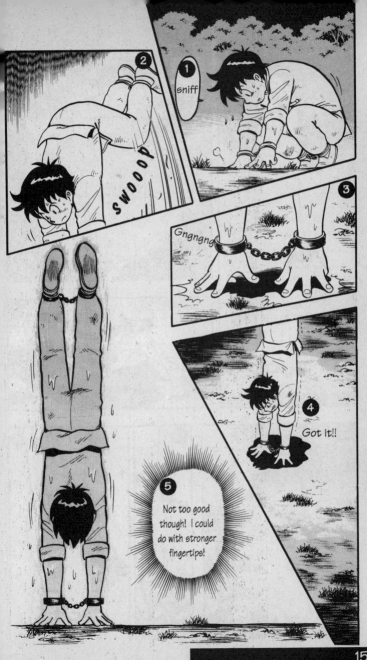

156

Three fingers!

BLEAAAKK

Ulp.

It hurts.

cough hack

CRUMP

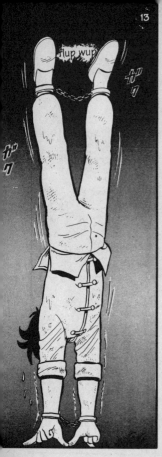

Yahaaah!

I've had too much wine! I need a nap.

I wonder if that little brat's dead yet?

!!

8 There's something wrong with that kid! He should be afraid.

7 He's standing upside-down!

9

10

splot

splot

splot

11

② Now I need to find a weak point in Shockwave Kung Fu itself.

③ I'LL ONLY HAVE ONE CHANCE!!

Lord Zangi,
Lord Dohko,
the sun
has risen.

Good.
Shall we
begin?

The End of Chapter Three

Chapter Four
Breaking Point

Whoooo

Temple boy shall set an example.

Yessir!

All of Song Jia village have come to watch!

Good.

Come here!

1. I expect you're all waiting for me to kill the one who defeated my brother Ryuhi, but a mere execution would be too boring.

2. He will be killed before your very eyes.

3. I want you all to see him suffer and die.

4 Dammit...I can still feel the wounds inside me!

7 But if he can't move, he can't defend himself! They're so cruel!

6 Chinmi's badly hurt! Look, he can't even move!

5

10 Let us begin!

9 And only one!

8 I've got one chance for survivial.

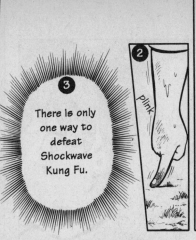

1

2 plink

3 There is only one way to defeat Shockwave Kung Fu.

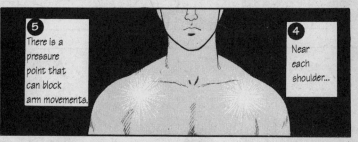

5 There is a pressure point that can block arm movements.

4 Near each shoulder...

7 But I can't see those points on Zangi.

6 I need to hit both points at once!

8 They'll only become visible when he spreads his arms for the shockwave attack.

9 That is the moment I must strike.

12 The inside of my skull will turn into sludge!

11 I'll end up like that melon!

10 But if I leave it too late....

Hhhr-hhr Hhhr-hhr

Are you ready, little monk?

Hhhr-hhr

haa
haaa
haaaa

Chinmi.

174

9

11 I'll only get one chance.

10 Ah...I see you've already assumed the posture of the condemned man.

13 Enough of this!

12 I must control my breathing.

178

THWAP

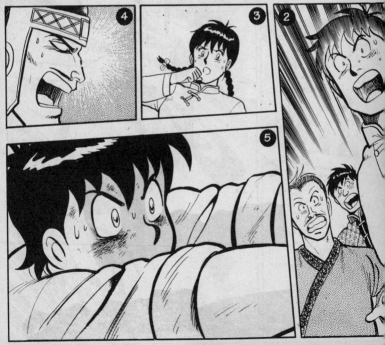

Got
him!!

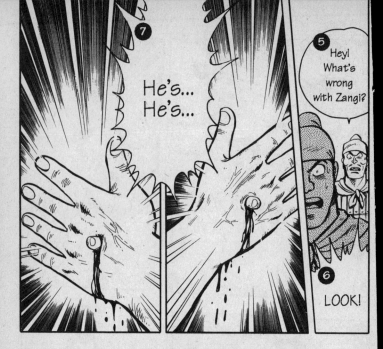

187

189

Chinmi?!

Agh...

crump

Get him again! Quick!

Chinmi! Get up!

The wounds would not have healed in one night.

I think Shockwave Kung Fu has won after all...

Hhhr-hhr Hhhr-hhr

How? I have no way of getting past his defences. I've tried already!

Hhhr-hhr

Zangi's coming.

plik plik

Aaah!

crump

THWACK

Lord Zangi is losing strength in his arms!

Chinmi! His arms are still moving! How can that be?

blip blip blip

He still has enough power to defeat the kid!

Whaaat?

scrape

14 Here he comes again.

15 But what can I do?... I can't even run away!

16 WHAT CAN I DO?!

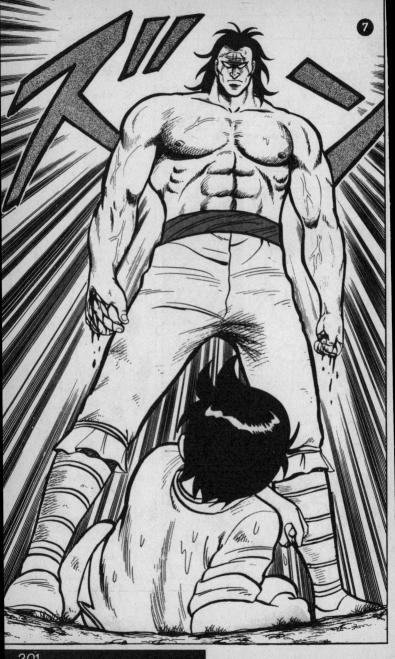

You have caused me enough trouble.

It's time to kill you.

thwip

9

Use your opponent's strength against him!!

8

Hhhr

7

Now...

11

The rain only carves the hole if it concentrates on one specific point...

13

Do not meet him head on. Let him meet himself!

12

thwip

2

Use your opponent's strength against him!

1

slap

3

One specific point...

5

4

Oh Chinmi... What have I done?

6

Heh heh heh

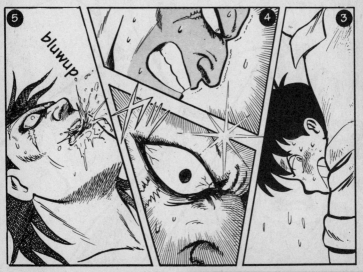

212

① Where is he?!
I thought he
couldn't move!

②

③ Too bad
for you,
ugly!

④ Wong!

⑦ *shing*

I'LL...!!

⑥ We took the
hint when
Gokuwa arrived
on his own!

⑤ Sorry
if we're
late.

216

7

Throw down your weapons!

6

9 Dailin!

Mummy!

8 There's nowhere to run!

11 KACHINK SPEENK POKK

10 Help!

14 Thank you.

13 Heehee.

12 Thank you.

Too kind.

217

1 Take them off to the magistrate.

2 Chinmi!!

3 Mei Ling!!

4 I'm so proud of you!

5 ‥‥ ‥‥

Eek

6

218

End of Book 5
The adventures of IRONFIST Chinmi are
continued in Book 6: Blind fury

Published in Great Britain 1995
by Bloomsbury Children's Books
2 Soho Square, London W1V 5DE

First published in Japan 18 May 1985 and
as at 25 January 1993, reprinted 20 times
by Kodansha, Tokyo.
English publication rights arranged through Kodansha.

English Edition
Translated by Jonathan Clements

A CIP catalogue record for this book
is available from the British Library

ISBN 0-7475-2100-X
10 9 8 7 6 5 4 3 2 1

Printed and bound in Denmark
by Norhaven A/S

Chapter One
Attack of the Black Flame